Penguin and Octopus Play

and
play

by Shelley Harwayne
Illustrated by Tammie Lyon

SCHOLASTIC INC.
New York   Toronto   London   Auckland   Sydney
Mexico City   New Delhi   Hong Kong   Buenos Aires

ISBN-13: 978-0-545-16787-1
ISBN-10: 0-545-16787-6

Text copyright © 2009 by Shelley Harwayne
Illustrations copyright © 2009 by Scholastic Inc.

12 11 10 9 8 7 6 5 4 3   10 11 12 13 14/0
Printed in the U.S.A.
First printing, September 2009

We **play and play**.

We **play** with balls **and** blocks.

We **play** with bikes **and** tops.

We **play** with cars **and** dolls.

We **play** with trains **and** balloons.

I **play** with all the toys!